# Why the Reindeer has a Velvet Nose

By Robin Page · Illustrated by Annie Tempest

**BIRD'S FARM
BOOKS**

Robin Page was born and bred on the farm where he still lives. Wildlife – the birds, animals, insects and flowers around him have been a life-long love. He has written twenty-five books for adults, and contributes to various national newspapers and magazines. He is Director and founder of The Countryside Restoration Trust.

Annie Tempest lives in Norfolk and is one of England's much-loved cartoonists. She is best known for her characters Lord and Lady Tottering, an aristocratic couple in gentle decline, whose doings can be followed in the British weekly magazine *Country Life*. Annie exhibits her work at The O'Shea Gallery, London. The Gallery sponsors and promotes her books, prints and products worldwide. For further information visit **www.tottering.com**

**FOR SARAH**

First published in 2002 by Bird's Farm Books
Barton, Cambs. CB3 7AG

Text © Robin Page, 2002
Illustrations © Annie Tempest, 2002

ISBN 0 905232 21 6

Designed by Jim Reader

Design and production in association with
Book Production Consultants plc
25–27 High Street, Chesterton, Cambridge CB4 1ND

Printed and bound by Proost NV, Turnhout, Belgium

In those dim and distant days before Father
Christmas had a sleigh, all raindeer had bright red
noses. Rudolph the Red-Nosed Raindeer had a bright
red nose and so did Reginald, Robert, Rupert, Rodney,
Robin and Renee. It was traditional in those dim and
distant days before people sang Christmas carols for
all the boy
raindeer – the
bulls – to have
names beginning
with R. It was harder
for the girl raindeer
– the cows – as there
are far fewer girls'
names beginning
with R.

So they were allowed to use names that would rhyme; there were Rosey, Posey and Josie. There were Ray, May, Fay and in those days even Gay. There were Robina, Sabrina and Serafina. There was also Roberta – but sadly nothing would rhyme with Roberta. In those days too there was a strange girl's name of Rucket, but as it would only rhyme with Bucket, nobody used it, and today it is almost forgotten.

But although the raindeer had bright red noses, they did not have bright red toeses; they had hooves at the end of their legs – big, solid, hard hooves, just right for walking over rocks and climbing to the top of high mountains.

Toeses, particularly bare toeses, are not good for climbing mountains, and raindeer do not wear shoes.

In those dim and distant days before Christmas pudding had been invented, raindeer loved climbing mountains. The world was hotter then – much warmer than today – and that is why the raindeer had bright red noses – they were burnt red by the sun, and in those dim and distant days there was no sunburn cream.

Most animals then, and now, had cold, wet noses. There were big, wet, cold noses and there were small, wet, cold noses, belonging to dogs and hogs, cows and sows, mares and hares, lambs and rams, goats and stoats and even cats and bats; but the raindeer's nose was warm, dry and bright red. All the other animals got their noses wet in bogs and marshes and puddles and ponds, but the raindeer did not like getting their noses wet and so their noses glowed up and showed up. They even shone red on moonlit nights.

With their thick, hairy coats and their beautiful but heavy antlers, they got so hot that during the summer

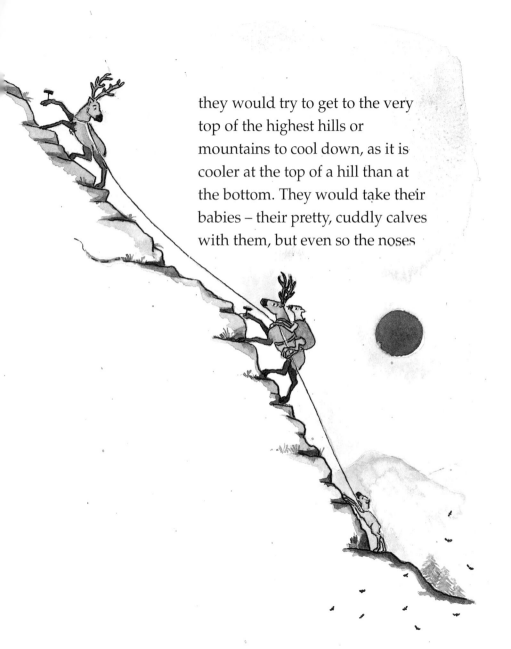

they would try to get to the very
top of the highest hills or
mountains to cool down, as it is
cooler at the top of a hill than at
the bottom. They would take their
babies – their pretty, cuddly calves
with them, but even so the noses

of the calves gradually turned bright red too. Up in the mountains they would go looking for shade and cool, away from the flies. Up there they liked drier food than that scoffed by the dogs and hogs, cows and sows, hares and mares, lambs and rams, goats and stoats and even cats and bats. They would eat more delicately; they would browse on special herbs and grasses, leaves and lichen, and they loved nibbling at moss.

In those dim and distant days before anybody had sung *Jingle Bells*, the raindeer's favourite food was lichen – which is rather like moss, but hairier. It comes in curls and whirls, and clumps and humps, and the reindeer still find it delicious today. They would pronounce it as lichen or "liken", and when they found it they would say a little rhyme: "We love licking lichen; we lick lovely lichen; we like lovely lichen and we want it for our tea". They were not good poets, but it was the best they could do.

But although the raindeer liked lichen; and even though they got on well with the dogs and hogs, cows and sows, mares and hares, lambs and rams, goats and stoats and even the cats and bats, the one thing they liked best of all was rain. They loved the rain – it wet them, it washed them, it cooled them, and even their red noses ceased to glow quite so much.

Singing in the rain...

Because they longed for the rain, every day Rudolph would ask one of his wives – raindeer bulls as big as Rudolph often have more than one wife – "Is it going to rain dear?" They would reply: "I hope it's going to rain dear", "We certainly need the rain dear". "When is it going to rain dear?" "If only it would rain dear."
"Can I hear it rain dear?" The dogs and hogs, cows and sows, mares and hares, lambs and rams, goats and stoats, and even the cats and bats, got so fed up with all the "is it going to rain dears?", every single day, that they called Rudolph and his wives, and his children and his brothers and his sisters "raindeer" – and they have been called raindeer – well, almost raindeer, ever since.

Now in those dim and distant days before crackers were pulled at Christmas, the raindeer were very happy whenever the rain came. The big drops of water cooled their hot, red noses; but their thick, smart coats kept them dry but cool.

In those dim and distant days before there had ever been a Christmas, the raindeer were glad they had antlers. Their antlers made them look beautiful and fierce, and with all those spikes they were just right for protection against wily wolves and scary Scotsmen.

Scotsmen – in those dim and distant days?

Yes Scotsmen! In those dim and distant days before bagpipes had been invented, raindeer lived in Scotland. They lived in many other countries too, such as Finland, Sweden, Norway and Lapland, but they lived in Scotland as well and liked it, apart from the wolves and the Scotsmen. Wolves of course no longer live in Scotland, but Scotsmen do.

The trouble was that the wolves and the Scotsmen liked raindeer, particularly to eat. They liked nice tender raindeer for breakfast as raindeer sausages; for dinner as raindeer stew; for tea as raindeer sandwiches and for supper as Rudolph burgers. Oh yes, raindeer were considered to be very tasty in those dim and distant days before turkeys were stuffed for Christmas dinner.

As long as the raindeer had their antlers they were safe. The wolves were wary and the Scotsmen were very careful; they had to be, because in those dim and distant days when the weather was still warm, all Scotsmen wore skirts. They weren't called skirts – as Scotsmen did not like wearing women's clothes – so they were called "kilts", to be different. In case the wind blew from the north and lifted their kilts above their heads, they also wore big, baggy knickers made from empty bags of porridge, to keep themselves looking decent.

But strangely, the raindeer did not always have antlers, and then they were in danger from the wily wolves and the scary Scotsmen. Each year their antlers would grow and grow and get heavier and heavier and then, when they were almost too heavy for the raindeer to keep their heads up, the antlers would fall off. First, the bulls would lose their beautiful antlers, and even Rudolph's antlers would fall to the ground. After that, the cows would lose their lovely antlers. They fell off, so that they could grow a new pair; and as soon as one pair fell to the ground, another pair began to sprout. It was then, while they were antlerless, that they were in the greatest danger from the wily wolves and the scary Scotsmen.

DOE!
-A DEER-
A FEMALE DEER

RAY!
YOU'VE DROPPED
YOUR FLIPPING
ANTLERS
ON MY KITCHEN
FLOOR AGAIN!

In those dim and distant days before Scotsmen ate haggis instead of raindeer, Rudolph and his friends need not have worried about being without their antlers because the Scotsmen were more interested in

collecting the fallen antlers than chasing dinner. They loved collecting antlers because they were so useful in their caves and huts. They used them as coat hangers, hat-stands, walking sticks and even umbrellas.

That's right, the umbrella was first invented in Scotland. Just as the raindeer loved the rain, so the Scotsmen hated the rain, and if they were out walking and a storm came, at the first spots of rain they would shout: "Up yer kilts!" Using old antlers, they would hoist their kilts above their heads. Some even had holes in their hats so the antlers stood up unaided; with the kilts spread out aloft it was like standing under a cluster of little tents, and the Scotsmen kept dry – just as long as the wind did not blow. If the wind did blow, then sometimes their kilts were blown away and they had to run home in their baggy porridge bag knickers and they got soaked.

Although the Scottish men were gruff, and their ginger hair made them seem gruffer, the Scottish women were pretty, polite and happy. They had happy-sounding names like Fiona, Morna and Morag, and they liked singing. They did not like their husbands and sons getting wet with their silly umbrellas and they tried to get them to wear raincoats instead – the world's first "macs". Each morning as the men and boys went out to hunt or look for antlers, they would say; "Don't forget your mac Donald" or "Have you got your mac Duff?" and "Don't forget your mac Tavish". Today, many Scottish names still start with "Mac" to remind them to take their coats, as Scotland is very wet.

But in those dim and distant days before anybody had heard of ice cream, the world slowly began to get colder and colder and the knickers of the Scotsmen got baggier and baggier and longer and longer to keep their legs warm. In the hot days of the warm world, nature had helped many Scotsmen keep cool; their

bright ginger hair had dropped out to stop them getting too hot.

Now, the bald Scotsmen shivered and shook with cold and they made woolly hats to keep their heads warm. The cold rain turned to snow, the snow turned to ice, and the earth moved into the Ice Age.

The Scotsmen shivered and so did the dogs and hogs, cows and sows, mares and hares, lambs and rams, goats and stoats and even the cats and bats. They were all so cold that they moved south looking for the sun. The wolves were not so good at geography and they moved north, while the raindeer stayed exactly where they were and they got colder and colder.

They did move from the top of the valleys to the bottom, and they had to take great long strides in the deep snow to avoid slipping. In fact their strides were so long that with each one, a tendon (part of their leg) just above the hoof went *click, click, click, click*. The raindeer moved down the valley and the noise helped them to follow one another in the snow. If you hear a raindeer walk today, it still has its "click" and this helps the herd to stay together.

It was so cold that their noses glowed not from the heat, but from the cold; they throbbed with cold. Each day they had to search for lichen; they no longer said their little rhyme about "licking lovely lichen" because it was too cold to lick. Every day they had to put their bare noses in the snow to sniff, snuffle and search for lichen and their noses grew redder and redder and Rudolph's grew the reddest of them all.

Then, when they were feeling cold and desperate two astonishing things happened. Deep down in the coldest snow, the raindeer found great strands of bushy lichen that looked and felt like a velvet beard; before, they had only ever seen it growing in the trees. But the lichen was still in the trees; the snow was so deep that the raindeer were actually eating from the trees. It was lovely lichen, and they enjoyed it so much that they started reciting their little rhyme again: "We love licking lichen; we lick lovely lichen; we like lovely lichen and we want it for our tea".

It felt warmer than the other lichens and it soothed the cold noses of Reginald, Robert, Rupert, Rodney, Robin and Renee, and Rosey, Posey, Josie, Ray, May, Fay, Gay, Robina, Sabrina and Seraphina.

Each day they stood with their noses in the snow, soothing them with the velvet lichen. And as their

noses touched the lichen, so special juices flowed from the lichen onto their noses and gradually their noses began to grow hair just like the lichen; thick, warm and velvety. As the hair began growing, the noses stopped glowing and the hair grew thicker and thicker until it was just like velvet. Their noses grew so warm that even on the coldest day, in the coldest snow, they never even started to glow and that is how the raindeer got its velvet nose.

Ever since those not quite so dim and distant days raindeer have had velvet noses, although every so often a little bull raindeer is born with a bald nose that still turns red in the cold. Because of tradition his name is Rudolph and he is always a proud and handsome raindeer.

But this is not the end of the story, for not only did the ice come, but it stayed and even the sea turned to ice. Now just as the Scotsmen moved south, so the Laplanders from Norway, Sweden and Finland also moved south. They walked across the frozen sea all the way to Scotland. Some arrived with their own

raindeer, but others had none at all. They were glad to find Rudolph and his friends, as it reminded them of home. Rudolph and his friends were glad to see the Laplanders, as they were so much kinder than the

Scotsmen. So, it was agreed that if the raindeer helped to pull the sledges of the Laps, the Laplanders would help to protect the raindeer.

Just like horses today, the Laps put reins on the raindeer so that they could pull the sledges, and ever since then the raindeer have been called "reindeer", and that is why Father Christmas uses them to pull his sleigh every Christmas Eve.

Slowly, very slowly, the Ice Age began to fade away and the weather became warmer. The Laps wanted to return to their proper home and they had to go before the sea-ice melted. The reindeer decided to go with them, and left Scotland to the returning Scotsmen. They journeyed north across the melting ice and just made land, before walking all the way to Lapland where there were forests, moors, bogs and lichen galore.

Then, as it was no longer the dim and distant past, something of great importance happened. A little baby was born in Bethlehem and people started singing carols, giving presents and celebrating Christmas. It was then, too, that Father Christmas began to use reindeer to pull his sleigh; reindeer with warm, velvet noses.

But even now that is not the end of the story, for in the most recent and reasonable past a Laplander who loved reindeer, Mickel Utsi, went on holiday to Scotland. It reminded him of home and he thought that such a beautiful wild place should have beautiful

wild reindeer. So he brought reindeer back to Scotland. They still came back over the sea, but this time in a boat. He brought them back to Reindeer House in the Cairngorms, near Aviemore, in 1952 and that is where reindeer can still be seen in Scotland today.

Scotsmen still look at the reindeer in a funny way, and wonder why they no longer have red noses. The reindeer still look at the Scotsmen in a funny way, and smile little furtive smiles to themselves. They know a secret that could help bald Scotsmen to grow hair, but they keep their secret to themselves. We know their secret and we must keep it to ourselves too.